This book belongs to:

_____

BEING
LESS
MEAN TO
MYSELF

SELF-CARE JOURNAL
FOR TEENS

Date: _____

Morning mood: 😊 🙂 😐 🙁 😣

	Did I do it?	Mood before?	Mood after?

What's one thing I can do today for....

Fun? ✶

Health? \|\|/

Relaxation? ☀

What am I beating myself up for today? 〰️

≡♡≡ How can I think more positively about it?

Was I kind to myself today?
(circle below)

Yes   Kind of   Not really

Evening mood: 😊 🙂 😐 🙁 😣

Date: _____

Morning mood: 🙂 🙂 😐 🙁 😣

	Did I do it?	Mood before?	Mood after?

What's one thing I can do today for....

Fun? ✳

Health? ⋎⋎⟋

Relaxation? ☼

What am I beating myself up for today? 〰〰

☽♡☾ How can I think more positively about it?

Was I kind to myself today?
(circle below)

Yes   Kind of   Not really

Evening mood: 🙂 🙂 😐 🙁 😣

Date: _____

Morning mood: 😊 🙂 😐 🙁 😣

	Did I do it?	Mood before?	Mood after?
			✓ (1 - 10)

What's one thing I can do today for....

Fun? ✳

Health? ＼Ｖ∕

Relaxation? ☀

What am I beating myself up for today? 〰

How can I think more positively about it?

Was I kind to myself today?
(circle below)

Yes   Kind of   Not really

Evening mood: 😊 🙂 😐 🙁 😣

Date: _____

Morning mood: 😊 🙂 😐 🙁 😣

	Did I do it?	Mood before?	Mood after?
✓ (1 - 10)			

What's one thing I can do today for....

Fun? ✳

Health? 〵〵⁄

Relaxation? ☀

What am I beating myself up for today? 〰〰

How can I think more positively about it?

Was I kind to myself today?
(circle below)

Yes   Kind of   Not really

Evening mood: 😊 🙂 😐 🙁 😣

Date: _____

Morning mood: 🙂 🙂 😐 🙁 😣

	Did I do it?	Mood before?	Mood after?

What's one thing I can do today for....

Fun? ✳

Health? \\\\⁄

Relaxation? ☀

What am I beating myself up for today? 〰

How can I think more positively about it?

Was I kind to myself today?
(circle below)

Yes   Kind of   Not really

Evening mood: 🙂 🙂 😐 🙁 😣

Date: _____

(1 - 10)

Morning mood: 🙂 🙂 😐 🙁 😣

	Did I do it?	Mood before?	Mood after?

What's one thing I can do today for....

Fun? ✳

Health? �

Relaxation? ☀

What am I beating myself up for today? 〰

How can I think more positively about it?

Was I kind to myself today?
(circle below)

Yes   Kind of   Not really

Evening mood: 🙂 🙂 😐 🙁 😣

Date: _____

Morning mood: 😊 🙂 😐 🙁 😣

What's one thing I can do today for....

	Did I do it?	Mood before?	Mood after?
Fun? ✳			
Health? ||⁄			
Relaxation? ☀			

What am I beating myself up for today? 〰

How can I think more positively about it?

Was I kind to myself today?
(circle below)

Yes   Kind of   Not really

Evening mood: 😊 🙂 😐 🙁 😣

Date: _____

Morning mood: 😊 🙂 😐 🙁 😣

✓ (1 - 10)

Did I do it?
Mood before?
Mood after?

What's one thing I can do today for....

Fun? ✳

Health? 🖌

Relaxation? ☀

What am I beating myself up for today?

_____

💡 How can I think more positively about it?

_____

Was I kind to myself today?
(circle below)

Yes   Kind of   Not really

Evening mood: 😊 🙂 😐 🙁 😣

Date: _____

Morning mood: 😌 🙂 😐 🙁 😣

	Did I do it?	Mood before?	Mood after?
	✓ (1 - 10)		

What's one thing I can do today for....

Fun? ✳

Health? \\\\/

Relaxation? 🌞

What am I beating myself up for today? 〰️

☼♡☼ How can I think more positively about it?

Was I kind to myself today?
(circle below)

Yes   Kind of   Not really

Evening mood:

Date: _____

Morning mood: 😊 🙂 😐 🙁 😣

	Did I do it?	Mood before?	Mood after?
		✓ (1 - 10)	

What's one thing I can do today for....

Fun? ✳

Health?

Relaxation? ☀

What am I beating myself up for today?

How can I think more positively about it?

Was I kind to myself today?
(circle below)

Yes   Kind of   Not really

Evening mood: 😊 🙂 😐 🙁 😣

Date: _____

Morning mood: 😊 🙂 😐 🙁 😣

Did I do it?　Mood before?　Mood after?

What's one thing I can do today for....

Fun? ✳

_____

Health? ⋁⋁⁄

_____

Relaxation? ☀

_____

What am I beating myself up for today?

_____

How can I think more positively about it?

_____

Was I kind to myself today?
(circle below)

Yes　　　　　　　Kind of　　　　　　　Not really

Evening mood: 😊 🙂 😐 🙁 😣

Date: _____

Morning mood: 🙂 😊 😐 🙁 😣

What's one thing I can do today for....

Fun? ✳

Health? 〵〵〴

Relaxation? ☀

	✓ (1 - 10)	
Did I do it?	Mood before?	Mood after?

What am I beating myself up for today? ✎

How can I think more positively about it?

Was I kind to myself today?
(circle below)

Yes   Kind of   Not really

Evening mood:

Date: _____

Morning mood: 😊 🙂 😐 🙁 😣

What's one thing I can do today for....

	Did I do it?	Mood before?	Mood after?
Fun? ✳			
Health? ||/			
Relaxation? ☀			

What am I beating myself up for today? 〰️

_____

≡♡≡ How can I think more positively about it?

_____

Was I kind to myself today?
(circle below)

Yes   Kind of   Not really

Evening mood: 😊 🙂 😐 🙁 😣

Date: _____

	Did I do it?	Mood before?	Mood after?
✓ (1 - 10)			

Morning mood: 😊 🙂 😐 🙁 😣

What's one thing I can do today for....

Fun? ✳

Health? \\|/

Relaxation? ☀

What am I beating myself up for today? 〰

How can I think more positively about it?

Was I kind to myself today?
(circle below)

Yes   Kind of   Not really

Evening mood:

Date: _____

Morning mood: 🙂 🙂 😐 🙁 😣

What's one thing I can do today for....

Fun? ✳

Health? 〵〵〳

Relaxation? ☀

What am I beating myself up for today? 〰

≡♡≡ How can I think more positively about it?

Was I kind to myself today?
(circle below)

Yes   Kind of   Not really

Evening mood: 🙂 🙂 😐 🙁 😣

Date: _____

Morning mood: 😊 🙂 😐 🙁 😣

What's one thing I can do today for....

Fun? ✳

Health? 〵〵⁄

Relaxation? ☀

✓ (1 - 10)

Did I do it?
Mood before?
Mood after?

What am I beating myself up for today? 〰

≡♡≡ How can I think more positively about it?

Was I kind to myself today?
(circle below)

Yes   Kind of   Not really

Evening mood: 😊 🙂 😐 🙁 😣

Date: _____

Morning mood: 😊 🙂 😐 🙁 😣

What's one thing I can do today for....

	Did I do it?	Mood before?	Mood after?
Fun? ✳			
Health? ||/			
Relaxation? ☼			

What am I beating myself up for today? 〰

⟡♡⟡ How can I think more positively about it?

Was I kind to myself today?
(circle below)

Yes   Kind of   Not really

Evening mood: 😊 🙂 😐 🙁 😣

Date: _____

✓ (1 - 10)

Morning mood: 😊 🙂 😐 🙁 😣

	Did I do it?	Mood before?	Mood after?

What's one thing I can do today for....

Fun? ✳

Health? ⑊

Relaxation? ☀

What am I beating myself up for today? 〰〰

How can I think more positively about it?

Was I kind to myself today?
(circle below)

Yes   Kind of   Not really

Evening mood:

Date: _____

Morning mood: 🙂 🙂 😐 🙁 😣

✓ (1 - 10)

Did I do it?
Mood before?
Mood after?

What's one thing I can do today for....

Fun? ✳

Health? ＼Ⅴ⁄

Relaxation? ☀

What am I beating myself up for today? 〰

≡♡≡ How can I think more positively about it?

Was I kind to myself today?
(circle below)

Yes   Kind of   Not really

Evening mood: 🙂 🙂 😐 🙁 😣

Date: _____

(1 - 10)

Morning mood: 😊 🙂 😐 🙁 😣

	Did I do it?	Mood before?	Mood after?

What's one thing I can do today for....

Fun? ✳

Health? ⑊

Relaxation? ☀

What am I beating myself up for today? 〰

How can I think more positively about it?

Was I kind to myself today?
(circle below)

Yes   Kind of   Not really

Evening mood: 😊 🙂 😐 🙁 😣

Date: _____

Morning mood: 🙂 🙂 😐 🙁 😣

(1 - 10)

Did I do it? | Mood before? | Mood after?

What's one thing I can do today for....

Fun? ✳

Health?

Relaxation? ☀

What am I beating myself up for today? 〰

How can I think more positively about it?

Was I kind to myself today?
(circle below)

Yes　　　　　　Kind of　　　　　　Not really

Evening mood: 🙂 🙂 😐 🙁 😣

Date: _____

Morning mood: 🙂 🙂 😐 🙁 😣

	Did I do it?	Mood before?	Mood after?
✓ (1 - 10)			

What's one thing I can do today for....

Fun? ✳

Health? \\\ /

Relaxation? ☀

What am I beating myself up for today?

_____

How can I think more positively about it?

_____

Was I kind to myself today?
(circle below)

Yes   Kind of   Not really

Evening mood:

Date: _____

Morning mood: 😊 😊 😐 ☹ 😣

✓ (1 - 10)

Did I do it?
Mood before?
Mood after?

What's one thing I can do today for....

Fun? ✳

Health? �

Relaxation? ☀

What am I beating myself up for today?

How can I think more positively about it?

Was I kind to myself today?
(circle below)

Yes   Kind of   Not really

Evening mood: 😊 😊 😐 ☹ 😣

Date: _____

Morning mood: 🙂 🙂 😐 🙁 😣   ✓ (1 - 10)

What's one thing I can do today for....

	Did I do it?	Mood before?	Mood after?
Fun? ✳			
Health?			
Relaxation? ☀			

What am I beating myself up for today?

_____

How can I think more positively about it?

_____

Was I kind to myself today?
(circle below)

Yes   Kind of   Not really

Evening mood: 🙂 🙂 😐 🙁 😣

Date: _____

Morning mood: 😊 🙂 😐 🙁 😣

	Did I do it?	Mood before?	Mood after?
	✓ (1 - 10)		

What's one thing I can do today for....

Fun? ✳

Health? \\\╱

Relaxation? ☀️

What am I beating myself up for today? 〰️

≡♡≡ How can I think more positively about it?

Was I kind to myself today?
(circle below)

Yes   Kind of   Not really

Evening mood:

Date: _____

Morning mood: 😊 🙂 😐 🙁 😣

	Did I do it?	Mood before?	Mood after?
✓ (1 - 10)			

What's one thing I can do today for....

Fun? ✳

Health? \\\\/

Relaxation? ☀

What am I beating myself up for today? 〰

How can I think more positively about it?

Was I kind to myself today?
(circle below)

Yes   Kind of   Not really

Evening mood: 😊 🙂 😐 🙁 😣

Date: _____

Morning mood: 😊 🙂 😐 🙁 😣

	Did I do it?	Mood before?	Mood after?

What's one thing I can do today for....

Fun? ✳

Health? ＼Ｉ／

Relaxation? ☀

What am I beating myself up for today? 〰

♡ How can I think more positively about it?

Was I kind to myself today?
(circle below)

Yes   Kind of   Not really

Evening mood: 😊 🙂 😐 🙁 😣

Date: _____

 (1 - 10)

Morning mood: 😊 🙂 😐 🙁 😣

What's one thing I can do today for....

	Did I do it?	Mood before?	Mood after?
Fun? ✳			
Health? 〵〴〳			
Relaxation? ☀			

What am I beating myself up for today? ✐

☼♡☼ How can I think more positively about it?

Was I kind to myself today?
(circle below)

Yes   Kind of   Not really

Evening mood: 😊 🙂 😐 🙁 😣

Date: _____

Morning mood: 😊 😊 😐 🙁 😣

What's one thing I can do today for....

Fun? ✳

Health? \|\|/

Relaxation? ☀

	Did I do it?	Mood before?	Mood after?

✓ (1 - 10)

What am I beating myself up for today? 〰

≡♡≡ How can I think more positively about it?

Was I kind to myself today?
(circle below)

Yes   Kind of   Not really

Evening mood:

Date: _____

	Did I do it?	Mood before?	Mood after?
	✓ (1 - 10)		

Morning mood: 🙂 🙂 😐 🙁 😣

What's one thing I can do today for....

Fun? ✳

Health? \|/

Relaxation? ☀

What am I beating myself up for today?

How can I think more positively about it?

Was I kind to myself today?
(circle below)

Yes   Kind of   Not really

Evening mood: 🙂 🙂 😐 🙁 😣

Date: _____

Morning mood: 😊 😊 😐 🙁 😣

What's one thing I can do today for....

Fun? ✳

Health? ⋁⋁⁄

Relaxation? ☀

What am I beating myself up for today? 〰

≡♡≡ How can I think more positively about it?

Was I kind to myself today?
(circle below)

Yes   Kind of   Not really

Evening mood: 😊 😊 😐 🙁 😣

Date: _____

Morning mood: 😊 🙂 😐 🙁 😖

✓ (1 - 10)

Did I do it?
Mood before?
Mood after?

What's one thing I can do today for....

Fun? ✳

Health? 〲

Relaxation? ☀

What am I beating myself up for today? 〰

How can I think more positively about it?

Was I kind to myself today?
(circle below)

Yes   Kind of   Not really

Evening mood: 😊 🙂 😐 🙁 😖

Date: _____

Morning mood: 🙂 😊 😐 🙁 😣

✓ (1 - 10)

Did I do it?
Mood before?
Mood after?

What's one thing I can do today for....

Fun? ✳

Health? \|\/

Relaxation? ☀

What am I beating myself up for today? 〰

How can I think more positively about it?

Was I kind to myself today?
(circle below)

Yes   Kind of   Not really

Evening mood: 🙂 😊 😐 🙁 😣

Date: _____

Morning mood: 😊 🙂 😐 🙁 😣

What's one thing I can do today for....

	Did I do it?	Mood before?	Mood after?
Fun? ✳			
Health?			
Relaxation? ☀			

What am I beating myself up for today? 〰

How can I think more positively about it?

Was I kind to myself today?
(circle below)

Yes   Kind of   Not really

Evening mood: 😊 🙂 😐 🙁 😣

Date: _____

Morning mood: 🙂 🙂 😐 🙁 😖

What's one thing I can do today for....

	Did I do it?	Mood before?	Mood after?
			✓ (1 - 10)

Fun? ✳

Health? \|\|/

Relaxation? ☼

What am I beating myself up for today? 〰

≡♡≡ How can I think more positively about it?

Was I kind to myself today?
(circle below)

Yes   Kind of   Not really

Evening mood:

Date: _____

✓ (1 - 10)

Morning mood: 😊 🙂 😐 🙁 😣

What's one thing I can do today for....

Fun? ✳

Health?

Relaxation? ☀

	Did I do it?	Mood before?	Mood after?

What am I beating myself up for today? 〰

How can I think more positively about it?

Was I kind to myself today?
(circle below)

Yes   Kind of   Not really

Evening mood: 😊 🙂 😐 🙁 😣

Date: _____

Morning mood: 😊 🙂 😐 🙁 😣

What's one thing I can do today for....

Fun? ✳

Health? ＼Ｉ╱

Relaxation? ☀

What am I beating myself up for today? 〰

≡♡≡ How can I think more positively about it?

Was I kind to myself today?
(circle below)

Yes   Kind of   Not really

Evening mood:

Date: _____

Morning mood: 😊 🙂 😐 🙁 😣

What's one thing I can do today for....

	Did I do it?	Mood before?	Mood after?
✓ (1 - 10)			

Fun? ✳

Health? 〰

Relaxation? ☀

What am I beating myself up for today?

How can I think more positively about it?

Was I kind to myself today?
(circle below)

Yes　　　　　　Kind of　　　　　　Not really

Evening mood: 😊 🙂 😐 🙁 😣

Date: _____

Morning mood: 😊 🙂 😐 🙁 😣

What's one thing I can do today for....

	Did I do it?	Mood before?	Mood after?
	✓ (1 - 10)		

Fun? ✳

Health? \|/

Relaxation? ☀

What am I beating myself up for today? 〰

⚆♡⚆ How can I think more positively about it?

Was I kind to myself today?
(circle below)

Yes   Kind of   Not really

Evening mood: 😊 🙂 😐 🙁 😣

Date: _____

Morning mood: 😌 🙂 😐 🙁 😣

	Did I do it?	Mood before?	Mood after?

✓ (1 - 10)

What's one thing I can do today for....

Fun? ✳

Health?

Relaxation? ☀

What am I beating myself up for today?

=♡= How can I think more positively about it?

Was I kind to myself today?
(circle below)

Yes   Kind of   Not really

Evening mood: 😌 🙂 😐 🙁 😣

Date: _____

Morning mood: 😊 🙂 😐 🙁 😣

What's one thing I can do today for....

Fun? ✳

Health? ＼｜／

Relaxation? ☀

Did I do it? | Mood before? | Mood after?

What am I beating myself up for today? 〰〰

How can I think more positively about it?

Was I kind to myself today?
(circle below)

Yes   Kind of   Not really

Evening mood: 😊 🙂 😐 🙁 😣

Date: _____

Morning mood: 😋 🙂 😐 🙁 😫

	Did I do it?	Mood before?	Mood after?
			✓ (1 - 10)

What's one thing I can do today for....

Fun? ✳

Health? 〵〵〴

Relaxation? ☀

What am I beating myself up for today? 〰

≡♡≡ How can I think more positively about it?

Was I kind to myself today?
(circle below)

Yes   Kind of   Not really

Evening mood: 😋 🙂 😐 🙁 😫

Date: _____

Morning mood: 😊 🙂 😐 🙁 😣

What's one thing I can do today for....

Fun? ✳

Health? \|\|/

Relaxation? ☀

What am I beating myself up for today? 〰

How can I think more positively about it?

Was I kind to myself today?
(circle below)

Yes   Kind of   Not really

Evening mood: 😊 🙂 😐 🙁 😣

Date: _____

Morning mood: 🙂 🙂 😐 🙁 😣

What's one thing I can do today for....

	Did I do it?	Mood before?	Mood after?
	✓ (1 - 10)		

Fun? ✳

Health? \|\|/

Relaxation? ☀

What am I beating myself up for today? 〰

How can I think more positively about it?

Was I kind to myself today?
(circle below)

Yes   Kind of   Not really

Evening mood: 🙂 🙂 😐 🙁 😣

Date: _____

Morning mood: 😊 🙂 😐 🙁 😣

Did I do it?
Mood before?
Mood after?

What's one thing I can do today for....

Fun? ✳

Health? \\\/

Relaxation? ☀

What am I beating myself up for today? 〰

💗 How can I think more positively about it?

Was I kind to myself today?
(circle below)

Yes   Kind of   Not really

Evening mood: 😊 🙂 😐 🙁 😣

Date: _____

Morning mood: 😊 😊 😐 😟 😣

What's one thing I can do today for....

	Did I do it?	Mood before?	Mood after?
		✓ (1 - 10)	

Fun? ✳

Health? \|/

Relaxation? ☀

What am I beating myself up for today? 〰

How can I think more positively about it?

Was I kind to myself today?
(circle below)

Yes   Kind of   Not really

Evening mood: 😊 😊 😐 😟 😣

Date: _____

Morning mood: 😊 🙂 😐 🙁 😣

Did I do it? Mood before? Mood after?

What's one thing I can do today for....

Fun? ✳

Health? ⋁⋁⁄

Relaxation? ☀

What am I beating myself up for today? 〰

How can I think more positively about it? ♡

Was I kind to myself today?
(circle below)

Yes   Kind of   Not really

Evening mood: 😊 🙂 😐 🙁 😣

Date: _____

Morning mood: 😊 🙂 😐 🙁 😣

	Did I do it?	Mood before?	Mood after?

✓ (1 - 10)

What's one thing I can do today for....

Fun? ✳

Health? 〵〷〳

Relaxation? 🌞

What am I beating myself up for today? 〰️

≡♡≡ How can I think more positively about it?

Was I kind to myself today?
(circle below)

Yes   Kind of   Not really

Evening mood: 😊 🙂 😐 🙁 😣

Date: _____

Morning mood: 😊 🙂 😐 🙁 😣

What's one thing I can do today for....

	Did I do it?	Mood before?	Mood after?
			✓ (1 - 10)

Fun? ✳

Health? \|/

Relaxation? ☀

What am I beating myself up for today? 〰️

☼ How can I think more positively about it?

Was I kind to myself today?
(circle below)

Yes   Kind of   Not really

Evening mood: 😊 🙂 😐 🙁 😣

Date: _____

Morning mood: 😊 😊 😐 😟 😣

What's one thing I can do today for....

	Did I do it?	Mood before?	Mood after?
	✓ (1 - 10)		

Fun? ✳

Health? 〱〱〵

Relaxation? ☀

What am I beating myself up for today? 〰

☼ How can I think more positively about it?

Was I kind to myself today?
(circle below)

Yes   Kind of   Not really

Evening mood: 😊 😊 😐 😟 😣

Date: _____

Morning mood: 😊 😊 😐 😟 😣

✓ (1 - 10)

Did I do it?

Mood before?

Mood after?

What's one thing I can do today for....

Fun? ✳

Health?

Relaxation? ☀

What am I beating myself up for today?

How can I think more positively about it?

Was I kind to myself today?

(circle below)

Yes   Kind of   Not really

Evening mood: 😊 😊 😐 😟 😣

Date: _____

Morning mood: 🙂 😊 😐 🙁 😣

	Did I do it?	Mood before?	Mood after?

✓ (1 - 10)

What's one thing I can do today for....

Fun? ✳

Health?

Relaxation? ☀

What am I beating myself up for today? 〰

How can I think more positively about it?

Was I kind to myself today?
(circle below)

Yes   Kind of   Not really

Evening mood:

Date: _____

Morning mood: 😊 🙂 😐 🙁 😣

	Did I do it?	Mood before?	Mood after? (1 - 10)

What's one thing I can do today for....

Fun? ✳

Health?

Relaxation? ☀

What am I beating myself up for today? 〰

How can I think more positively about it?

Was I kind to myself today?
(circle below)

Yes   Kind of   Not really

Evening mood: 😊 🙂 😐 🙁 😣

Date: _____

Morning mood: 😊 🙂 😐 🙁 😣 ✓ (1 - 10)

What's one thing I can do today for....

	Did I do it?	Mood before?	Mood after?
Fun? ✳			
Health? ⅃⅃⫽			
Relaxation? ☀			

What am I beating myself up for today? 〰

≡♡≡ How can I think more positively about it?

Was I kind to myself today?
(circle below)

Yes   Kind of   Not really

Evening mood: 😊 🙂 😐 🙁 😣

Date: _____

Morning mood: 😊 🙂 😐 🙁 😣

✓ (1 - 10)

	Did I do it?	Mood before?	Mood after?

What's one thing I can do today for....

Fun? ✳

Health? \|/

Relaxation? ☀

What am I beating myself up for today? 〰

≡♡≡ How can I think more positively about it?

Was I kind to myself today?
(circle below)

Yes   Kind of   Not really

Evening mood: 😊 🙂 😐 🙁 😣

Date: _____

Morning mood: 😊 🙂 😐 🙁 😣

What's one thing I can do today for....

	Did I do it?	Mood before?	Mood after?
Fun? ✳			
Health? ||/			
Relaxation? ☼			

✓ (1 - 10)

What am I beating myself up for today? 〰

How can I think more positively about it?

Was I kind to myself today?
(circle below)

Yes   Kind of   Not really

Evening mood:

Date: _____

Morning mood: 😌 🙂 😐 🙁 😣

What's one thing I can do today for....

Fun? ✳

Health? \|/

Relaxation? ☀

What am I beating myself up for today? 〰

How can I think more positively about it?

Was I kind to myself today?
(circle below)

Yes   Kind of   Not really

Evening mood: 😌 🙂 😐 🙁 😣

Date: _____

Morning mood: 😃 🙂 😐 🙁 😣

What's one thing I can do today for....

| | ✓ (1 - 10) | | |
	Did I do it?	Mood before?	Mood after?
Fun? ✳			
Health? ||⁄			
Relaxation? ☀			

What am I beating myself up for today? 〰

How can I think more positively about it?

Was I kind to myself today?
(circle below)

Yes   Kind of   Not really

Evening mood: 😃 🙂 😐 🙁 😣

Date: _____

Morning mood: 😊 🙂 😐 🙁 😣

✓ (1 - 10)

Did I do it?

Mood before?

Mood after?

What's one thing I can do today for....

Fun? ✳

Health? ⑴⑴

Relaxation? ☀

What am I beating myself up for today? 〰

How can I think more positively about it?

Was I kind to myself today?
(circle below)

Yes   Kind of   Not really

Evening mood: 😊 🙂 😐 🙁 😣

Date: _____

Morning mood: 😊 🙂 😐 🙁 😣

What's one thing I can do today for....

	Did I do it?	Mood before?	Mood after?
	✓ (1 - 10)		

Fun? ✳

Health? \|\|⁄

Relaxation? ☀

What am I beating myself up for today? 〰

≡♡≡ How can I think more positively about it?

Was I kind to myself today?
(circle below)

Yes   Kind of   Not really

Evening mood: 😊 🙂 😐 🙁 😣

Date: _____

Morning mood: 😊 😊 😐 🙁 😣

	Did I do it?	Mood before?	Mood after?

✓ (1 - 10)

What's one thing I can do today for....

Fun? ✳

Health? \\\╱

Relaxation? ☀

What am I beating myself up for today? 〰

≡♡≡ How can I think more positively about it?

Was I kind to myself today?
(circle below)

Yes   Kind of   Not really

Evening mood:

Date: _____

Morning mood: 🙂 🙂 😐 🙁 😣

	Did I do it?	Mood before?	Mood after?
✓ (1 - 10)			

What's one thing I can do today for....

Fun? ✳

Health? \\\/

Relaxation? ☀

What am I beating myself up for today?

How can I think more positively about it?

Was I kind to myself today?
(circle below)

Yes　　　　　　　　Kind of　　　　　　　　Not really

Evening mood: 🙂 🙂 😐 🙁 😣

Date: _____

Morning mood: 😊 🙂 😐 🙁 😣

	Did I do it?	Mood before?	Mood after?

What's one thing I can do today for....

Fun? ✳

Health? ∖∣∕

Relaxation? ☀

What am I beating myself up for today? 〰

≡♡≡ How can I think more positively about it?

Was I kind to myself today?
(circle below)

Yes   Kind of   Not really

Evening mood:

Date: _____

Morning mood: 😊 🙂 😐 🙁 😣

✓ (1 - 10)

Did I do it?
Mood before?
Mood after?

What's one thing I can do today for....

Fun? ✳

Health? 〰〰

Relaxation? ☀

What am I beating myself up for today?

How can I think more positively about it?

Was I kind to myself today?
(circle below)

Yes   Kind of   Not really

Evening mood: 😊 🙂 😐 🙁 😣

Date: _____

Morning mood: 😕 🙂 😐 🙁 😣

What's one thing I can do today for....

	Did I do it?	Mood before?	Mood after?
Fun? ✳			
Health?			
Relaxation? ☀			

What am I beating myself up for today? 〰

How can I think more positively about it?

Was I kind to myself today?
(circle below)

Yes   Kind of   Not really

Evening mood: 😕 🙂 😐 🙁 😣

Date: _____

Morning mood: 🙂 😊 😐 🙁 😣

✓ (1 - 10)

Did I do it?
Mood before?
Mood after?

What's one thing I can do today for....

Fun? ✳

Health? \|/

Relaxation? ☀

What am I beating myself up for today?

_____

How can I think more positively about it?

_____

Was I kind to myself today?
(circle below)

Yes   Kind of   Not really

Evening mood: 🙂 😊 😐 🙁 😣

Date: _____

Morning mood: 😊 🙂 😐 ☹️ 😣

✓ (1 - 10)

Did I do it?
Mood before?
Mood after?

What's one thing I can do today for....

Fun? ✳

Health? \\\/

Relaxation? ☀

What am I beating myself up for today? 〰️

≡♡≡ How can I think more positively about it?

Was I kind to myself today?
(circle below)

Yes   Kind of   Not really

Evening mood: 😊 🙂 😐 ☹️ 😣

Date: _____

Morning mood: 😊 🙂 😐 🙁 😣

What's one thing I can do today for....

Fun? ✳

	Did I do it?	Mood before?	Mood after?
Fun?			
Health?			
Relaxation?			

Health? ⎀

Relaxation? ☀

What am I beating myself up for today? 〰

How can I think more positively about it?

Was I kind to myself today?
(circle below)

Yes   Kind of   Not really

Evening mood:

Date: _____

Morning mood: 😃 🙂 😐 🙁 😣

What's one thing I can do today for....

	Did I do it?	Mood before?	Mood after?
Fun? ✳			
Health?			
Relaxation?			

What am I beating myself up for today?

_____

How can I think more positively about it?

_____

Was I kind to myself today?
(circle below)

Yes   Kind of   Not really

Evening mood: 😃 🙂 😐 🙁 😣

Date: _____

 (1 - 10)

Morning mood: 😊 🙂 😐 🙁 😣

What's one thing I can do today for....

Fun? ✳

	Did I do it?	Mood before?	Mood after?
Fun? ✳			
Health? ||/			
Relaxation? ☀			

What am I beating myself up for today? 〰

_____

♡ How can I think more positively about it?

_____

Was I kind to myself today?
(circle below)

Yes   Kind of   Not really

Evening mood:

Date: _____

Morning mood: 😊 🙂 😐 🙁 😣

What's one thing I can do today for....

	Did I do it?	Mood before?	Mood after? (1 - 10) ✓
Fun? ✳			
Health? ||⁄			
Relaxation? ☀			

What am I beating myself up for today? 〰

_____

♡ How can I think more positively about it?

_____

Was I kind to myself today?
(circle below)

Yes   Kind of   Not really

Evening mood: 😊 🙂 😐 🙁 😣

Date: _____

Morning mood: 🙂 🙂 😐 🙁 😣

Did I do it?

Mood before?

Mood after?

What's one thing I can do today for....

Fun? ✳

Health? \|\|/

Relaxation? ☀

What am I beating myself up for today? 〰

How can I think more positively about it?

Was I kind to myself today?
(circle below)

Yes   Kind of   Not really

Evening mood: 🙂 🙂 😐 🙁 😣

Date: _____

Morning mood: 🙂 😊 😐 🙁 😣

	Did I do it?	Mood before?	Mood after?

What's one thing I can do today for....

Fun? ✳

Health? \\\\/

Relaxation? ☀

What am I beating myself up for today? 〰

How can I think more positively about it?

Was I kind to myself today?
(circle below)

Yes   Kind of   Not really

Evening mood: 🙂 😊 😐 🙁 😣

Date: _____

 (1 - 10)

Morning mood: 😊 😊 😐 🙁 😣

	Did I do it?	Mood before?	Mood after?
What's one thing I can do today for....			
Fun? ✳			
Health? ⎠⎠⎠			
Relaxation? ☀			

What am I beating myself up for today? 〰

_____

♡ How can I think more positively about it?

_____

Was I kind to myself today?
(circle below)

Yes   Kind of   Not really

Evening mood: 😊 😊 😐 🙁 😣

Date: _____

Morning mood: 😊 🙂 😐 🙁 😣

(1 - 10)

Did I do it?
Mood before?
Mood after?

What's one thing I can do today for....

Fun? ✳

Health? 〵〴〵

Relaxation? ☀

What am I beating myself up for today? 〰〰〰

≡♡≡ How can I think more positively about it?

Was I kind to myself today?
(circle below)

Yes   Kind of   Not really

Evening mood: 😊 🙂 😐 🙁 😣

Date: _____

Morning mood: 😊 🙂 😐 🙁 😣

Did I do it? | Mood before? | Mood after?

What's one thing I can do today for....

Fun? ✳

Health? \\\/

Relaxation? ☀

What am I beating myself up for today? 〰

⋛♡⋚ How can I think more positively about it?

Was I kind to myself today?
(circle below)

Yes   Kind of   Not really

Evening mood:

Date: _____

Morning mood: 😊 🙂 😐 🙁 😣   ✓ **(1 - 10)**

What's one thing I can do today for....

	Did I do it?	Mood before?	Mood after?
Fun? ✳			
Health? 川╱			
Relaxation? ☀			

What am I beating myself up for today? 〰

≡♡≡ How can I think more positively about it?

Was I kind to myself today?
(circle below)

Yes   Kind of   Not really

Evening mood:

Date: _____

Morning mood: 😊 🙂 😐 🙁 😣

	Did I do it?	Mood before?	Mood after?
✓ (1 - 10)			

What's one thing I can do today for....

Fun? ✳

Health? ⑊

Relaxation? ☀

What am I beating myself up for today? 〰

How can I think more positively about it?

Was I kind to myself today?
(circle below)

Yes　　　　　　Kind of　　　　　　Not really

Evening mood:

Date: _____

 (1 - 10)

Morning mood: 😊 😊 😐 🙁 😣

What's one thing I can do today for....

Fun? ✳

Health? \|/

Relaxation? 🌞

Did I do it?
Mood before?
Mood after?

What am I beating myself up for today? 〰️

♡ How can I think more positively about it?

Was I kind to myself today?
(circle below)

Yes   Kind of   Not really

Evening mood:

Date: _____

Morning mood: 😊 🙂 😐 🙁 😣

	Did I do it?	Mood before?	Mood after?

What's one thing I can do today for....

Fun? ✳

Health? ⑂

Relaxation? ☀

What am I beating myself up for today? 〰

How can I think more positively about it? ♡

Was I kind to myself today?
(circle below)

Yes   Kind of   Not really

Evening mood: 😊 🙂 😐 🙁 😣

Date: _____

Morning mood: 😊 🙂 😐 🙁 😣

✓ (1 - 10)

Did I do it?
Mood before?
Mood after?

What's one thing I can do today for....

Fun? ✳

Health? ﹨Ⅴ⁄

Relaxation? 🌞

What am I beating myself up for today? 〰

≡♡≡ How can I think more positively about it?

Was I kind to myself today?
(circle below)

Yes   Kind of   Not really

Evening mood:

Date: _____

✓ (1 - 10)

Morning mood: 😊 🙂 😐 🙁 😣

	Did I do it?	Mood before?	Mood after?

What's one thing I can do today for....

Fun? ✳

Health? 〵〵〴

Relaxation? ☼

What am I beating myself up for today? 〰

_____

≡♡≡ How can I think more positively about it?

_____

Was I kind to myself today?
(circle below)

Yes   Kind of   Not really

Evening mood:

Date: _____

Morning mood: 😊 😃 😐 🙁 😣

Did I do it?
Mood before?
Mood after?

What's one thing I can do today for....

Fun? ✳

Health? \|/

Relaxation? ☀

What am I beating myself up for today? 〰

⚡♡⚡ How can I think more positively about it?

Was I kind to myself today?
(circle below)

Yes   Kind of   Not really

Evening mood: 😊 😃 😐 🙁 😣

Date: _____

Morning mood: 😊 😊 😐 🙁 😣

	Did I do it?	Mood before?	Mood after?

What's one thing I can do today for....

Fun? ✳

Health? \|\|⁄

Relaxation? ☀

What am I beating myself up for today? 〰

≡♡≡ How can I think more positively about it?

Was I kind to myself today?
(circle below)

Yes   Kind of   Not really

Evening mood:

Date: _____

Morning mood: 😊 🙂 😐 🙁 😣

What's one thing I can do today for....

	Did I do it?	Mood before?	Mood after?
Fun? ✶			
Health? ||/			
Relaxation? ☀			

What am I beating myself up for today? 〰️

_____

≡♡≡ How can I think more positively about it?

_____

Was I kind to myself today?
(circle below)

Yes   Kind of   Not really

Evening mood: 😊 🙂 😐 🙁 😣

Date: ____________

Morning mood:

What's one thing I can do today for....

	Did I do it? ✓	Mood before? (1 - 10)	Mood after? (1 - 10)
Fun?			
Health?			
Relaxation?			

What am I beating myself up for today?

____

How can I think more positively about it?

____

Was I kind to myself today?

(circle below)

Yes Kind of Not really

Evening mood:

Date: _____

Morning mood: 😊 🙂 😐 🙁 😣

What's one thing I can do today for....

Fun? ✳

Health? 〵〵⁄

Relaxation? ☀

✓ (1 - 10)

Did I do it?

Mood before?

Mood after?

What am I beating myself up for today? ✎

≡♡≡ How can I think more positively about it?

Was I kind to myself today?
(circle below)

Yes   Kind of   Not really

Evening mood:

Date: _____

✓ (1 - 10)

Morning mood: 😊 🙂 😐 🙁 😣

What's one thing I can do today for....

Fun? ✳

	Did I do it?	Mood before?	Mood after?

Health?

Relaxation? ☀

What am I beating myself up for today? 〰

〰 How can I think more positively about it?

Was I kind to myself today?
(circle below)

Yes   Kind of   Not really

Evening mood:

Date: _____

Morning mood: 😊 🙂 😐 🙁 😣

| | Did I do it? | Mood before? | Mood after? |

What's one thing I can do today for....

Fun? ✳

Health? \l\/

Relaxation? ☀️

What am I beating myself up for today? 〰️

⚡♡⚡ How can I think more positively about it?

Was I kind to myself today?
(circle below)

Yes   Kind of   Not really

Evening mood:

Date: _____

✓ (1 - 10)

Morning mood: 😊 🙂 😐 🙁 😖

	Did I do it?	Mood before?	Mood after?

What's one thing I can do today for....

Fun? ✳

Health? \|/

Relaxation? ☀

What am I beating myself up for today? 〰

=♡= How can I think more positively about it?

Was I kind to myself today?
(circle below)

Yes   Kind of   Not really

Evening mood:

Date: _____

Morning mood: 😊 🙂 😐 🙁 😣

	✓ (1 - 10)
	Did I do it? / Mood before? / Mood after?

What's one thing I can do today for....

Fun? ✳

Health? ＼Ｖ／

Relaxation? 🌞

What am I beating myself up for today? 〰

～♡～ How can I think more positively about it?

Was I kind to myself today?
(circle below)

Yes   Kind of   Not really

Evening mood:

Date: _____

Morning mood: 🙂 🙂 😐 🙁 😣

What's one thing I can do today for....

	Did I do it?	Mood before?	Mood after?
Fun? ✳			
Health? ||/			
Relaxation? ☀			

What am I beating myself up for today? 〰

How can I think more positively about it?

Was I kind to myself today?
(circle below)

Yes   Kind of   Not really

Evening mood: 🙂 🙂 😐 🙁 😣

Date: _____

Morning mood: 😊 🙂 😐 🙁 😣

	Did I do it?	Mood before?	Mood after?

What's one thing I can do today for....

Fun? ✳

Health?

Relaxation? ☀

What am I beating myself up for today? 〰

≡♡≡ How can I think more positively about it?

Was I kind to myself today?
(circle below)

Yes   Kind of   Not really

Evening mood: 😊 🙂 😐 🙁 😣

Date: _____

Morning mood: 🙂 🙂 😐 🙁 😣

What's one thing I can do today for....

	Did I do it?	Mood before?	Mood after?
	✓ (1 - 10)		

Fun? ✳

Health? \|\|/

Relaxation? ☀

What am I beating myself up for today? 〰

How can I think more positively about it?

Was I kind to myself today?
(circle below)

Yes   Kind of   Not really

Evening mood: 🙂 🙂 😐 🙁 😣

Date: _____

Morning mood: 😌 🙂 😐 🙁 😣

What's one thing I can do today for....

Did I do it?
Mood before?
Mood after?

Fun? ✳

Health?

Relaxation? ☀

What am I beating myself up for today?

=♡= How can I think more positively about it?

Was I kind to myself today?
(circle below)

Yes   Kind of   Not really

Evening mood: 😌 🙂 😐 🙁 😣

Date: _____

✓ **(1 - 10)**

Morning mood: 😊 🙂 😐 🙁 😣

| | Did I do it? | Mood before? | Mood after? |

What's one thing I can do today for....

Fun? ✳

Health? ＼|／

Relaxation? ☀

What am I beating myself up for today? 〰️

≡♡≡ How can I think more positively about it?

Was I kind to myself today?
(circle below)

Yes   Kind of   Not really

Evening mood:

Date: _____

Morning mood: 😊 🙂 😐 🙁 😣

✓ (1 - 10)

Did I do it?
Mood before?
Mood after?

What's one thing I can do today for....

Fun? ✳

Health? \|/

Relaxation? ☀

What am I beating myself up for today? 〰

♡ How can I think more positively about it?

Was I kind to myself today?
(circle below)

Yes   Kind of   Not really

Evening mood: 😊 🙂 😐 🙁 😣